To:

_____

From:

_____

Date:

_____

If you would like to share how this journal has encouraged you or someone close to you, we would love to hear from you. Send us an email at: publisher@christianartgifts.com

Put your hope in the Lord. Travel steadily along His path.

Ps. 37:34

_____

_____

_____

_____

_____

_____

_____

_____

_____

_____

_____

_____

_____

_____

_____

_____

_____

_____

_____

If you make the Lord your refuge,
He will order His angels to protect you wherever you go.

Ps. 91:9-11

_____

_____

_____

_____

_____

_____

_____

_____

_____

_____

_____

_____

_____

_____

_____

_____

_____

_____

O God, You will keep in perfect peace all who trust in You,
all whose thoughts are fixed on You!

Isa. 26:3

I ponder all Your great works, O Lord, and think about what You have done.

Ps. 143:5

_____

_____

_____

_____

_____

_____

_____

_____

_____

_____

_____

_____

_____

_____

_____

_____

_____

_____

_____

_____

**May the words of my mouth and the meditation of my heart
be pleasing to You, O Lord, my rock and my Redeemer.**

Ps. 19:14

"I know the plans I have for you," declares the Lord,
plans to prosper you and not to harm you,
plans to give you hope and a future."

Jer. 29:11

Your word is a lamp to guide my feet and a light for my path.

Ps. 119:105

Show me the right path, O Lord; point out the road for me to follow.
Lead me by Your truth and teach me, for You are the God who saves me.

Ps. 25:4-5

The Lord says, "I will guide you along the best pathway for your life.
I will advise you and watch over you."

Ps. 32:8

_____

_____

_____

_____

_____

_____

_____

_____

_____

_____

_____

_____

_____

_____

_____

_____

_____

_____

Jesus said, "I am with you always, to the very end of the age."

Matt. 28:20

Commit to the Lord whatever you do,
and He will establish your plans.

Prov. 16:3

_____

_____

_____

_____

_____

_____

_____

_____

_____

_____

_____

_____

_____

_____

_____

_____

_____

Whether you turn to the right or to the left, your ears will hear a voice behind you, saying, "This is the way; walk in it."

Isa. 30:21

_____

_____

_____

_____

_____

_____

_____

_____

_____

_____

_____

_____

_____

_____

_____

_____

_____

_____

_____

_____

God said, "My presence will go with you.
I'll see the journey to the end."

Exod. 33:14

May the God of hope fill you with all joy and peace in believing,
so that by the power of the Holy Spirit you may abound in hope.

Rom. 15:13

God is our refuge and strength, a very present help in trouble.

Ps. 46:1

Cast your cares on the Lord and He will sustain you.

Ps. 55:22

Be strong and take heart, all you who hope in the Lord.

Ps. 31:24

_____

_____

_____

_____

_____

_____

_____

_____

_____

_____

_____

_____

_____

_____

_____

_____

_____

_____

I can do everything through Christ, who gives me strength.

Phil. 4:13

_____

_____

_____

_____

_____

_____

_____

_____

_____

_____

_____

_____

_____

_____

_____

_____

_____

_____

_____

Be strong and courageous. Do not be afraid; do not be discouraged, for the Lord your God will be with you wherever you go.

Josh. 1:9

Fix your thoughts on what is true, and honorable, and right, and pure, and lovely, and admirable. Think about things that are excellent and worthy of praise.

Phil. 4:8

Do not be anxious about anything ... the peace of God,
which transcends all understanding, will guard your hearts
and your minds in Christ Jesus.

Phil. 4:6-7

_____

_____

_____

_____

_____

_____

_____

_____

_____

_____

_____

_____

_____

_____

_____

_____

_____

_____

_____

_____

_____

Those who trust in the Lord will find new strength. They will
soar high on wings like eagles. They will run and not grow weary.
They will walk and not faint.

Isa. 40:31

_____

_____

_____

_____

_____

_____

_____

_____

_____

_____

_____

_____

_____

_____

_____

_____

_____

_____

"Do not fear, for I am with you; do not be dismayed, for I am your God.
I will strengthen you and help you; I will uphold you with My
righteous right hand."

Isa. 41:10

_____

_____

_____

_____

_____

_____

_____

_____

_____

_____

_____

_____

_____

_____

_____

_____

_____

_____

_____

_____

"Be still, and know that I am God!"

Ps. 46:10

The Lord your God is in your midst, a mighty One who will save;
He will rejoice over you with gladness; He will quiet you by His love;
He will exult over you with loud singing.

Zeph. 3:17

_____

_____

_____

_____

_____

_____

_____

_____

_____

_____

_____

_____

_____

_____

_____

_____

_____

_____

_____

The Lord is my strength and song, and He has become my salvation.

Exod. 15:2

_____

_____

_____

_____

_____

_____

_____

_____

_____

_____

_____

_____

_____

_____

_____

_____

_____

_____

You, Lord, are the light that keeps me safe.
You protect me, and I have no fears.

Ps. 27:1

_____

_____

_____

_____

_____

_____

_____

_____

_____

_____

_____

_____

_____

_____

_____

_____

_____

_____

_____

You will be secure, because there is hope;
you will look about you and take your rest in safety.

Job 11:18

_____

_____

_____

_____

_____

_____

_____

_____

_____

_____

_____

_____

_____

_____

_____

_____

_____

_____

Trust in the Lord with all your heart and lean not on your own understanding;
in all your ways submit to Him, and He will make your paths straight.

Prov. 3:5-6

_____

_____

_____

_____

_____

_____

_____

_____

_____

_____

_____

_____

_____

_____

_____

_____

_____

_____

Put your hope in the Lord. Travel steadily along His path.

Ps. 37:34

_____

_____

_____

_____

_____

_____

_____

_____

_____

_____

_____

_____

_____

_____

_____

_____

_____

If you make the Lord your refuge,
He will order His angels to protect you wherever you go.

Ps. 91:9-11

O God, You will keep in perfect peace all who trust in You,
all whose thoughts are fixed on You!

Isa. 26:3

I ponder all Your great works, O Lord, and think about what You have done.

Ps. 143:5

**May the words of my mouth and the meditation of my heart
be pleasing to You, O Lord, my rock and my Redeemer.**

Ps. 19:14

_____

_____

_____

_____

_____

_____

_____

_____

_____

_____

_____

_____

_____

_____

_____

_____

_____

_____

_____

"I know the plans I have for you," declares the Lord,
plans to prosper you and not to harm you,
plans to give you hope and a future."

Jer. 29:11

_____

_____

_____

_____

_____

_____

_____

_____

_____

_____

_____

_____

_____

_____

_____

_____

_____

_____

_____

_____

_____

Your word is a lamp to guide my feet and a light for my path.

Ps. 119:105

Show me the right path, O Lord; point out the road for me to follow.
Lead me by Your truth and teach me, for You are the God who saves me.

Ps. 25:4-5

The Lord says, "I will guide you along the best pathway for your life.
I will advise you and watch over you."

Ps. 32:8

Jesus said, "I am with you always, to the very end of the age."

Matt. 28:20

_____

_____

_____

_____

_____

_____

_____

_____

_____

_____

_____

_____

_____

_____

_____

_____

_____

_____

Commit to the Lord whatever you do,
and He will establish your plans.

Prov. 16:3

_____

_____

_____

_____

_____

_____

_____

_____

_____

_____

_____

_____

_____

_____

_____

_____

_____

_____

_____

Whether you turn to the right or to the left, your ears will hear a voice
behind you, saying, "This is the way; walk in it."

Isa. 30:21

God said, "My presence will go with you.
I'll see the journey to the end."

Exod. 33:14

_____

_____

_____

_____

_____

_____

_____

_____

_____

_____

_____

_____

_____

_____

_____

_____

_____

_____

_____

_____

God is our God for ever and ever;
He will be our Guide even to the end.

Ps. 48:14

May the God of hope fill you with all joy and peace in believing,
so that by the power of the Holy Spirit you may abound in hope.

Rom. 15:13

_____

_____

_____

_____

_____

_____

_____

_____

_____

_____

_____

_____

_____

_____

_____

_____

_____

_____

_____

_____

God is our refuge and strength, a very present help in trouble.

Ps. 46:1

Cast your cares on the Lord and He will sustain you.

Ps. 55:22

Be strong and take heart, all you who hope in the Lord.

Ps. 31:24

I can do everything through Christ, who gives me strength.

Phil. 4:13

_____

_____

_____

_____

_____

_____

_____

_____

_____

_____

_____

_____

_____

_____

_____

_____

_____

_____

Be strong and courageous. Do not be afraid; do not be discouraged,
for the Lord your God will be with you wherever you go.

Josh. 1:9

Fix your thoughts on what is true, and honorable, and right, and pure,
and lovely, and admirable. Think about things that are excellent
and worthy of praise.

Phil. 4:8

Do not be anxious about anything ... the peace of God,
which transcends all understanding, will guard your hearts
and your minds in Christ Jesus.

Phil. 4:6-7

_____

_____

_____

_____

_____

_____

_____

_____

_____

_____

_____

_____

_____

_____

_____

_____

_____

Those who trust in the Lord will find new strength. They will
soar high on wings like eagles. They will run and not grow weary.
They will walk and not faint.

Isa. 40:31

"Do not fear, for I am with you; do not be dismayed, for I am your God.
I will strengthen you and help you; I will uphold you with My
righteous right hand."

Isa. 41:10

The Lord your God is in your midst, a mighty One who will save;
He will rejoice over you with gladness; He will quiet you by His love;
He will exult over you with loud singing.

Zeph. 3:17

The Lord is my strength and song, and He has become my salvation.

Exod. 15:2

You, Lord, are the light that keeps me safe.
You protect me, and I have no fears.

Ps. 27:1

_____

_____

_____

_____

_____

_____

_____

_____

_____

_____

_____

_____

_____

_____

_____

_____

_____

_____

_____

**You will be secure, because there is hope;
you will look about you and take your rest in safety.**

Job 11:18

_____

_____

_____

_____

_____

_____

_____

_____

_____

_____

_____

_____

_____

_____

_____

_____

_____

_____

_____

Trust in the Lord with all your heart and lean not on your own understanding;
in all your ways submit to Him, and He will make your paths straight.

Prov. 3:5-6

If you make the Lord your refuge,
He will order His angels to protect you wherever you go.

Ps. 91:9-11

O God, You will keep in perfect peace all who trust in You,
all whose thoughts are fixed on You!

Isa. 26:3

I ponder all Your great works, O Lord, and think about what You have done.

Ps. 143:5

May the words of my mouth and the meditation of my heart
be pleasing to You, O Lord, my rock and my Redeemer.

Ps. 19:14

"I know the plans I have for you," declares the Lord,
plans to prosper you and not to harm you,
plans to give you hope and a future."

Jer. 29:11

Your word is a lamp to guide my feet and a light for my path.

Ps. 119:105

Show me the right path, O Lord; point out the road for me to follow.
Lead me by Your truth and teach me, for You are the God who saves me.

Ps. 25:4-5

_____

_____

_____

_____

_____

_____

_____

_____

_____

_____

_____

_____

_____

_____

_____

_____

_____

_____

**Do not be afraid; do not be discouraged,
for the Lord your God will be with you wherever you go.**

Josh. 1:9

The Lord says, "I will guide you along the best pathway for your life.
I will advise you and watch over you."

Ps. 32:8

_____

_____

_____

_____

_____

_____

_____

_____

_____

_____

_____

_____

_____

_____

_____

_____

_____

_____

_____

Jesus said, "I am with you always, to the very end of the age."

Matt. 28:20

Commit to the Lord whatever you do,
and He will establish your plans.

Prov. 16:3

God said, "My presence will go with you.
I'll see the journey to the end."

Exod. 33:14

God is our God for ever and ever;
He will be our Guide even to the end.

Ps. 48:14

May the God of hope fill you with all joy and peace in believing,
so that by the power of the Holy Spirit you may abound in hope.

Rom. 15:13

God is our refuge and strength, a very present help in trouble.

Ps. 46:1

_____

_____

_____

_____

_____

_____

_____

_____

_____

_____

_____

_____

_____

_____

_____

_____

_____

_____

Cast your cares on the Lord and He will sustain you.

Ps. 55:22

I can do everything through Christ, who gives me strength.

Phil. 4:13

_____

_____

_____

_____

_____

_____

_____

_____

_____

_____

_____

_____

_____

_____

_____

_____

_____

_____

Be strong and courageous. Do not be afraid; do not be discouraged,
for the Lord your God will be with you wherever you go.

Josh. 1:9

Fix your thoughts on what is true, and honorable, and right, and pure, and lovely, and admirable. Think about things that are excellent and worthy of praise.

Phil. 4:8

The Lord is faithful, and He will strengthen and protect you.

2 Thess. 3:3

_____

_____

_____

_____

_____

_____

_____

_____

_____

_____

_____

_____

_____

_____

_____

_____

Do not be anxious about anything ... the peace of God,
which transcends all understanding, will guard your hearts
and your minds in Christ Jesus.

Phil. 4:6-7

Those who trust in the Lord will find new strength. They will
soar high on wings like eagles. They will run and not grow weary.
They will walk and not faint.

Isa. 40:31

"Do not fear, for I am with you; do not be dismayed, for I am your God.
I will strengthen you and help you; I will uphold you with My
righteous right hand."

Isa. 41:10

_____

_____

_____

_____

_____

_____

_____

_____

_____

_____

_____

_____

_____

_____

_____

_____

_____

The Lord your God is in your midst, a mighty One who will save;
He will rejoice over you with gladness; He will quiet you by His love;
He will exult over you with loud singing.

Zeph. 3:17

_____

_____

_____

_____

_____

_____

_____

_____

_____

_____

_____

_____

_____

_____

_____

_____

_____

_____

The Lord is my strength and song, and He has become my salvation.

Exod. 15:2

_____

_____

_____

_____

_____

_____

_____

_____

_____

_____

_____

_____

_____

_____

_____

_____

_____

_____

You, Lord, are the light that keeps me safe.
You protect me, and I have no fears.

Ps. 27:1

_____

_____

_____

_____

_____

_____

_____

_____

_____

_____

_____

_____

_____

_____

_____

_____

_____

_____

_____

_____

You will be secure, because there is hope;
you will look about you and take your rest in safety.

Job 11:18

_____

_____

_____

_____

_____

_____

_____

_____

_____

_____

_____

_____

_____

_____

_____

_____

_____

_____

Trust in the Lord with all your heart and lean not on your own understanding;
in all your ways submit to Him, and He will make your paths straight.

Prov. 3:5-6

_____

_____

_____

_____

_____

_____

_____

_____

_____

_____

_____

_____

_____

_____

_____

_____

_____

_____

_____

Put your hope in the Lord. Travel steadily along His path.

Ps. 37:34

If you make the Lord your refuge,
He will order His angels to protect you wherever you go.

Ps. 91:9-11

_____

_____

_____

_____

_____

_____

_____

_____

_____

_____

_____

_____

_____

_____

_____

_____

_____

_____

_____

O God, You will keep in perfect peace all who trust in You,
all whose thoughts are fixed on You!

Isa. 26:3

_____

_____

_____

_____

_____

_____

_____

_____

_____

_____

_____

_____

_____

_____

_____

_____

_____

_____

I ponder all Your great works, O Lord, and think about what You have done.

Ps. 143:5

May the words of my mouth and the meditation of my heart
be pleasing to You, O Lord, my rock and my Redeemer.

Ps. 19:14

"I know the plans I have for you," declares the Lord,
plans to prosper you and not to harm you,
plans to give you hope and a future."

Jer. 29:11

_____

_____

_____

_____

_____

_____

_____

_____

_____

_____

_____

_____

_____

_____

Your word is a lamp to guide my feet and a light for my path.

Ps. 119:105

_____

_____

_____

_____

_____

_____

_____

_____

_____

_____

_____

_____

_____

_____

_____

_____

_____

Show me the right path, O Lord; point out the road for me to follow.
Lead me by Your truth and teach me, for You are the God who saves me.

Ps. 25:4-5

_____

_____

_____

_____

_____

_____

_____

_____

_____

_____

_____

_____

_____

_____

_____

_____

_____

_____

_____

_____

**Do not be afraid; do not be discouraged,
for the Lord your God will be with you wherever you go.**

Josh. 1:9

_____

_____

_____

_____

_____

_____

_____

_____

_____

_____

_____

_____

_____

_____

_____

_____

_____

_____

_____

The Lord says, "I will guide you along the best pathway for your life.
I will advise you and watch over you."

Ps. 32:8

_____

_____

_____

_____

_____

_____

_____

_____

_____

_____

_____

_____

_____

_____

_____

_____

_____

_____

_____

_____

_____

Jesus said, "I am with you always, to the very end of the age."

Matt. 28:20

_____

_____

_____

_____

_____

_____

_____

_____

_____

_____

_____

_____

_____

_____

_____

_____

_____

_____

Commit to the Lord whatever you do,
and He will establish your plans.

Prov. 16:3

Whether you turn to the right or to the left, your ears will hear a voice behind you, saying, "This is the way; walk in it."

Isa. 30:21

_____

_____

_____

_____

_____

_____

_____

_____

_____

_____

_____

_____

_____

_____

_____

_____

_____

God said, "My presence will go with you.
I'll see the journey to the end."

Exod. 33:14

_____

_____

_____

_____

_____

_____

_____

_____

_____

_____

_____

_____

_____

_____

_____

_____

_____

_____

_____

God is our God for ever and ever;
He will be our Guide even to the end.

Ps. 48:14

_____

_____

_____

_____

_____

_____

_____

_____

_____

_____

_____

_____

_____

_____

_____

_____

_____

May the God of hope fill you with all joy and peace in believing,
so that by the power of the Holy Spirit you may abound in hope.

Rom. 15:13

_____

_____

_____

_____

_____

_____

_____

_____

_____

_____

_____

_____

_____

_____

_____

_____

_____

_____

God is our refuge and strength, a very present help in trouble.

Ps. 46:1

Cast your cares on the Lord and He will sustain you.

Ps. 55:22

Be strong and take heart, all you who hope in the Lord.

Ps. 31:24

I can do everything through Christ, who gives me strength.

Phil. 4:13

Be strong and courageous. Do not be afraid; do not be discouraged,
for the Lord your God will be with you wherever you go.

Josh. 1:9

_____

_____

_____

_____

_____

_____

_____

_____

_____

_____

_____

_____

_____

_____

_____

_____

_____

_____

_____

_____

Fix your thoughts on what is true, and honorable, and right, and pure,
and lovely, and admirable. Think about things that are excellent
and worthy of praise.

Phil. 4:8

The Lord is faithful, and He will strengthen and protect you.

2 Thess. 3:3

Do not be anxious about anything ... the peace of God,
which transcends all understanding, will guard your hearts
and your minds in Christ Jesus.

Phil. 4:6-7

Those who trust in the Lord will find new strength. They will
soar high on wings like eagles. They will run and not grow weary.
They will walk and not faint.

Isa. 40:31

_____

_____

_____

_____

_____

_____

_____

_____

_____

_____

_____

_____

_____

_____

_____

_____

_____

_____

"Do not fear, for I am with you; do not be dismayed, for I am your God.
I will strengthen you and help you; I will uphold you with My
righteous right hand."

Isa. 41:10

The Lord your God is in your midst, a mighty One who will save;
He will rejoice over you with gladness; He will quiet you by His love;
He will exult over you with loud singing.

Zeph. 3:17

_____

_____

_____

_____

_____

_____

_____

_____

_____

_____

_____

_____

_____

_____

_____

_____

_____

_____

The Lord is my strength and song, and He has become my salvation.

Exod. 15:2

You, Lord, are the light that keeps me safe.
You protect me, and I have no fears.

Ps. 27:1

_____

_____

_____

_____

_____

_____

_____

_____

_____

_____

_____

_____

_____

_____

_____

_____

_____

_____

_____

_____

**You will be secure, because there is hope;
you will look about you and take your rest in safety.**

Job 11:18

_____

_____

_____

_____

_____

_____

_____

_____

_____

_____

_____

_____

_____

_____

_____

_____

_____

_____

_____

Trust in the Lord with all your heart and lean not on your own understanding;
in all your ways submit to Him, and He will make your paths straight.

Prov. 3:5-6

Put your hope in the Lord. Travel steadily along His path.

Ps. 37:34

_____

_____

_____

_____

_____

_____

_____

_____

_____

_____

_____

_____

_____

_____

_____

_____

_____

_____

_____

_____

If you make the Lord your refuge,
He will order His angels to protect you wherever you go.

Ps. 91:9-11

O God, You will keep in perfect peace all who trust in You,
all whose thoughts are fixed on You!

Isa. 26:3

_____

_____

_____

_____

_____

_____

_____

_____

_____

_____

_____

_____

_____

_____

_____

_____

_____

_____

_____

I ponder all Your great works, O Lord, and think about what You have done.

Ps. 143:5

May the words of my mouth and the meditation of my heart
be pleasing to You, O Lord, my rock and my Redeemer.

Ps. 19:14

_____

_____

_____

_____

_____

_____

_____

_____

_____

_____

_____

_____

_____

_____

_____

_____

"I know the plans I have for you," declares the Lord,
plans to prosper you and not to harm you,
plans to give you hope and a future."

Jer. 29:11

Show me the right path, O Lord; point out the road for me to follow.
Lead me by Your truth and teach me, for You are the God who saves me.

Ps. 25:4-5

Do not be afraid; do not be discouraged,
for the Lord your God will be with you wherever you go.

Josh. 1:9

The Lord says, "I will guide you along the best pathway for your life.
I will advise you and watch over you."

Ps. 32:8

Jesus said, "I am with you always, to the very end of the age."

Matt. 28:20

Commit to the Lord whatever you do,
and He will establish your plans.

Prov. 16:3

_____

_____

_____

_____

_____

_____

_____

_____

_____

_____

_____

_____

_____

_____

_____

_____

_____

_____

_____

Whether you turn to the right or to the left, your ears will hear a voice
behind you, saying, "This is the way; walk in it."

Isa. 30:21

God said, "My presence will go with you.
I'll see the journey to the end."

Exod. 33:14

God is our God for ever and ever;
He will be our Guide even to the end.

Ps. 48:14

May the God of hope fill you with all joy and peace in believing,
so that by the power of the Holy Spirit you may abound in hope.

Rom. 15:13

God is our refuge and strength, a very present help in trouble.

Ps. 46:1

Cast your cares on the Lord and He will sustain you.

Ps. 55:22

I can do everything through Christ, who gives me strength.

Phil. 4:13

Be strong and courageous. Do not be afraid; do not be discouraged, for the Lord your God will be with you wherever you go.

Josh. 1:9

Fix your thoughts on what is true, and honorable, and right, and pure, and lovely, and admirable. Think about things that are excellent and worthy of praise.

Phil. 4:8

_____

_____

_____

_____

_____

_____

_____

_____

_____

_____

_____

_____

_____

_____

_____

_____

_____

_____

_____

The Lord is faithful, and He will strengthen and protect you.

2 Thess. 3:3

_____

_____

_____

_____

_____

_____

_____

_____

_____

_____

_____

_____

_____

_____

_____

_____

_____

Do not be anxious about anything ... the peace of God,
which transcends all understanding, will guard your hearts
and your minds in Christ Jesus.

Phil. 4:6-7

_____

_____

_____

_____

_____

_____

_____

_____

_____

_____

_____

_____

_____

_____

_____

_____

_____

_____

_____

_____

_____

Those who trust in the Lord will find new strength. They will
soar high on wings like eagles. They will run and not grow weary.
They will walk and not faint.

Isa. 40:31

"Do not fear, for I am with you; do not be dismayed, for I am your God.
I will strengthen you and help you; I will uphold you with My
righteous right hand."

Isa. 41:10

_____

_____

_____

_____

_____

_____

_____

_____

_____

_____

_____

_____

_____

_____

_____

_____

_____

_____

_____

"Be still, and know that I am God!"

Ps. 46:10

_____

_____

_____

_____

_____

_____

_____

_____

_____

_____

_____

_____

_____

_____

_____

_____

_____

The Lord your God is in your midst, a mighty One who will save;
He will rejoice over you with gladness; He will quiet you by His love;
He will exult over you with loud singing.

Zeph. 3:17

_____

_____

_____

_____

_____

_____

_____

_____

_____

_____

_____

_____

_____

_____

_____

_____

_____

The Lord is my strength and song, and He has become my salvation.

Exod. 15:2

You, Lord, are the light that keeps me safe.
You protect me, and I have no fears.

Ps. 27:1